THE ULTIMATE

MOTHER GOOSE COLLECTION

Nursery Rhyme Lyric Book

Twin Sisters Productions, LLC
4710 Hudson Drive, Stow, OH 44224 USA
www.twinsisters.com 1-800-248-8946

ISBN-13: 978-159922-591-3

Hickory Dickory Dock

Hickory dickory dock.
The mouse ran up the clock.
The clock struck **one**.
The mouse ran down.
Hickory dickory dock!

Hickory dickory dock.
The mouse ran up the clock.
The clock struck **two**
and down he flew.
Hickory dickory dock!

Hickory dickory dock.
The mouse ran up the clock.
The clock struck **three**.
The mouse said, "Watch me!"
Hickory dickory dock!

Hickory dickory dock.
The mouse ran up the clock.
The clock struck **four**.
The mouse said, "Once more!"
Hickory dickory dock!

Hickory dickory dock.
The mouse ran up the clock
The clock struck **five**.
The mouse survived.
Hickory dickory dock!

Little Boy Blue come blow your horn.
The sheep's in the meadow.

The cow's in the corn.

Where is the boy who looks after the sheep?
He's under the haystack fast asleep.

Find your way to the boy who should be looking after the sheep.

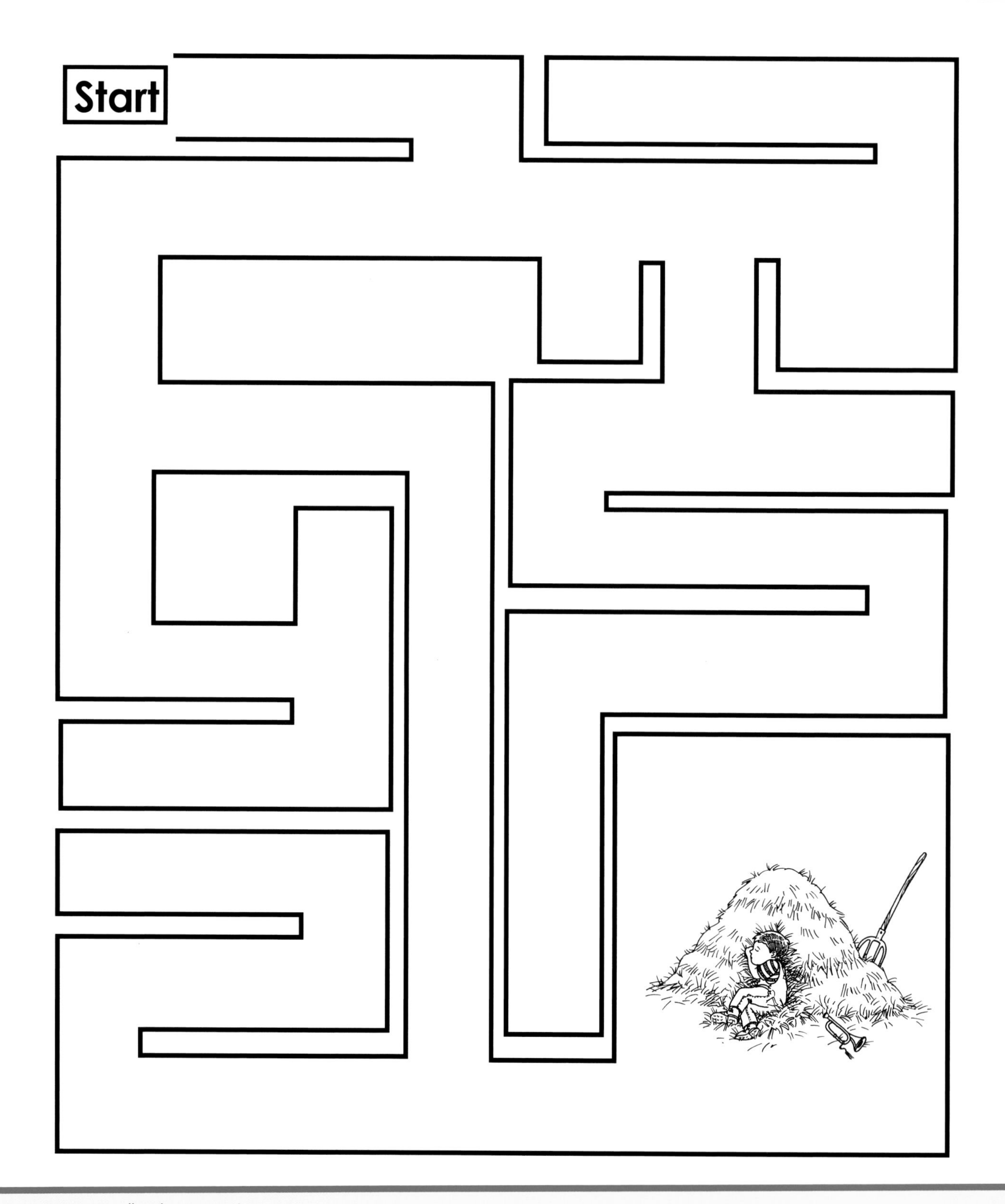

Hey diddle, diddle,
the cat and the fiddle,

the cow jumped
over the moon.

The little dog laughed
to see such a sport

and the dish ran away
with the spoon.

Draw the cow jumping over the moon.

Little Bo Peep

Little Bo Peep has lost her sheep
and can't tell where to find them.
Leave them alone and they'll come home,
wagging their tails behind them.

Help Little Bo Peep find her sheep. Draw a line from each sheep in order.

Mary Had a Little Lamb

Mary had a little lamb, little lamb, little lamb.
Mary had a little lamb. Its fleece was white as snow.

Everywhere that Mary went, Mary went, Mary went.
Everywhere that Mary went the lamb was sure to go.

It followed her to school one day, school one day, school one day.
It followed her to school one day which was against the rules.

Baa, Baa, Black Sheep

Baa, baa, black sheep,
have you any wool?
Yes sir, yes sir, three bags full.
One for my master, one for my dame,
and one for the little boy
who lives down the lane.

Master
Little Boy
Dame

Sing a Song of Sixpence

Sing a song of sixpence, a pocket full of rye,
Four-and-twenty blackbirds baked in a pie.

When the pie was opened,
the birds began to sing.
Wasn't that a dainty dish
to set before the king?

Count the blackbirds. How many are there?

There are ________ blackbirds.

The Mulberry Bush

Here we go 'round the mulberry bush, the mulberry bush, the mulberry bush.
Here we go 'round the mulberry bush, so early in the morning.

This is the way we wash our clothes, we wash our clothes, we wash our clothes.
This is the way we wash our clothes, so early in the morning.

Humpty Dumpty

Humpty Dumpty sat on a wall.
Humpty Dumpty had a great fall.
All the king's horses and all the king's men
couldn't put Humpty together again.

So some children came along singing Humpty's little song.
So they decided to think of a plan to put Humpty together again.

Working with some glue and tape, they gave Humpty a new shape.
Now Humpty Dumpty sits on a wall. Never again will Humpty fall.

Now when Humpty's story is told
a happy ending will unfold.
Working together to help Humpty mend—
working together, they helped a friend.

Write a number **1** under the picture of what happened first in the story.

Write a number **2** under the picture of what happened next.

Write a number **3** under the picture that shows how the story ends.

This Little Pig Went to Market

This little pig went to market.

This little pig stayed home.

This little pig had roast beef

This little pig had none.

This little pig cried, "Wee-wee-wee,"
all the way home!

Trace each line with your finger to learn what each little pig did.

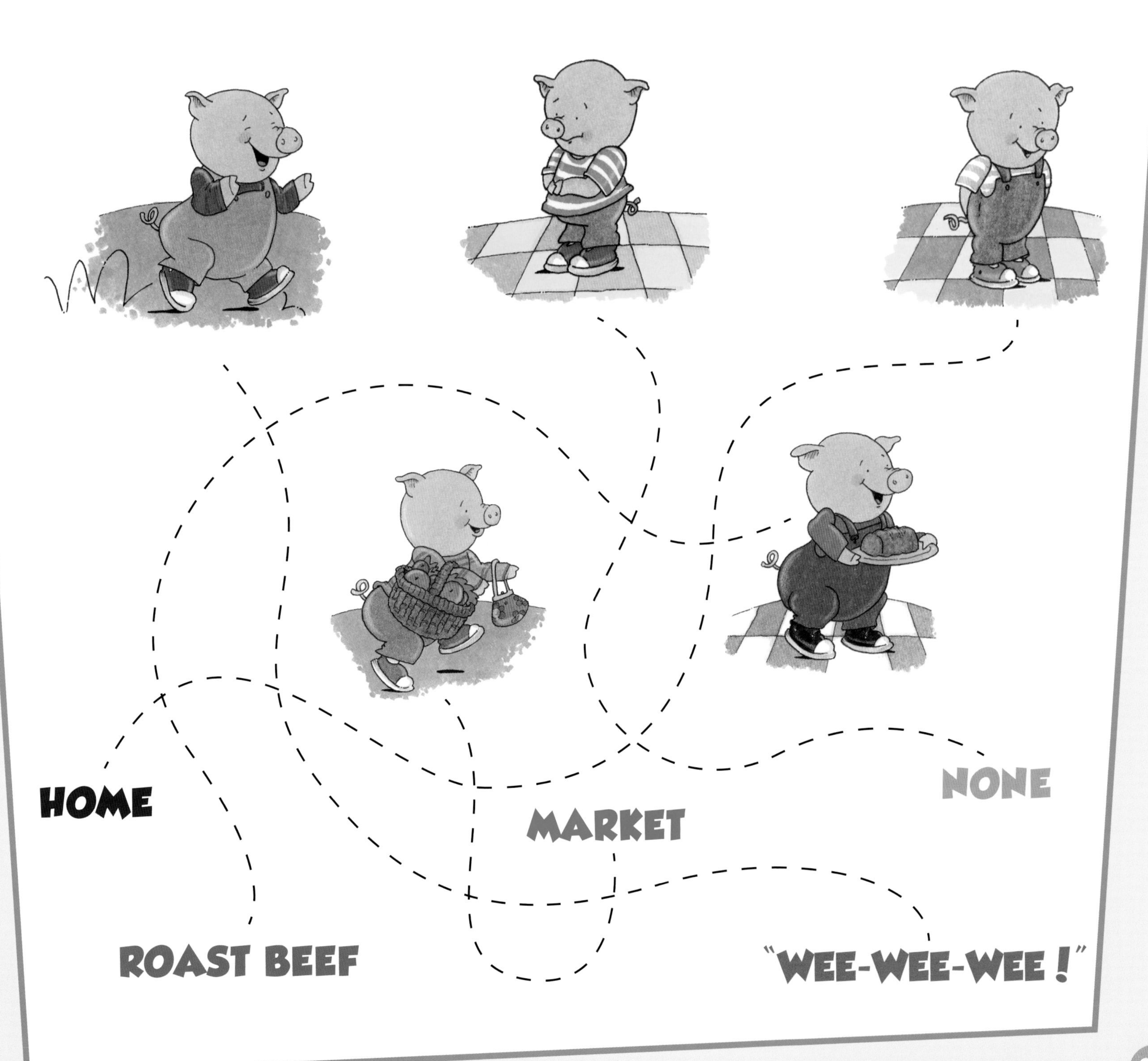

This Old Man

This old man, he played **one**.
He played knick knack on my **thumb**.
With a knick knack paddy
whack give a dog a bone,
this old man came rolling home.

This old man, he played **two**.
He played knick knack on my **shoe**.
With a knick knack paddy
whack give a dog a bone,
this old man came rolling home.

This old man, he played **three**.
He played knick knack on my **knee**.
With a knick knack paddy
whack give a dog a bone,
this old man came rolling home.

This old man, he played **four**.
He played knick knack on my **door**.
With a knick knack paddy
whack give a dog a bone,
this old man came rolling home.

This old man, he played **five**.
He played knick knack on my **hive**.
With a knick knack paddy
whack give a dog a bone,
this old man came rolling home.

This old man, he played **six**.
He played knick knack on my **sticks**.
With a knick knack paddy
whack give a dog a bone,
this old man came rolling home.

This old man, he played **seven**.
He played knick knack up in **heaven**.
With a knick knack paddy
whack give a dog a bone,
this old man came rolling home.

This old man, he played **eight**.
He played knick knack on my **gate**.
With a knick knack paddy
whack give a dog a bone,
this old man came rolling home.

This old man, he played **nine**.
He played knick knack on my **spine**.
With a knick knack paddy
whack give a dog a bone,
this old man came rolling home.

This old man, he played **ten**.
He played knick knack once **again**.
With a knick knack paddy
whack give a dog a bone,
this old man came rolling home.

Little Miss Muffet

Little Miss Muffet sat on a tuffet

eating her curds and whey.

Along came a spider
and sat down beside her
and frightened
Miss Muffet away.

Draw what you think happened after Little Miss Muffet ran away from the spider.

Discuss how your child came to his or her conclusion.

Twinkle, Twinkle, Little Star

Twinkle, twinkle, little star,
how I wonder what you are.
Up above the world so high,
like a diamond in the sky.
Twinkle, twinkle, little star,
how I wonder what you are.

Trace the stars. When you finish each star, make a wish for someone special.

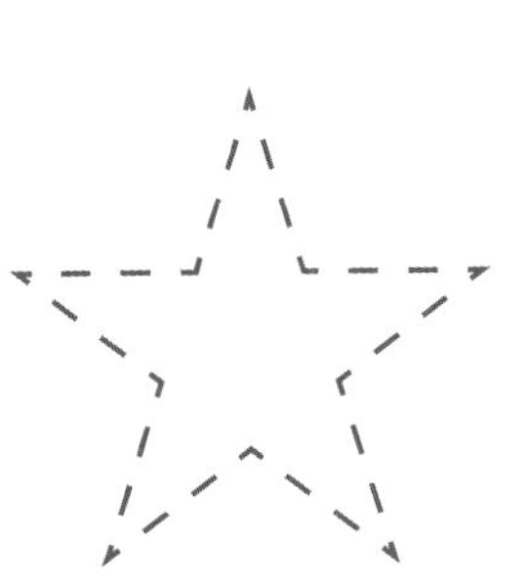
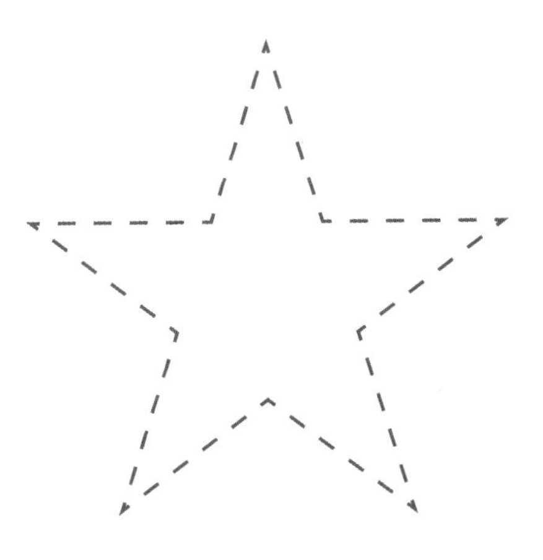

Rhyming Words

(Tune: The Mulberry Bush)

Sing the song below to learn about rhymes. Listen for the rhyming words. Think of other words that rhyme with the same ending sounds.

A rhyming word stays the same at the end,
the same at the end, the same at the end.
A rhyming word stays the same at the end.
You only change the beginning.

Cat and bat are rhyming words.
Hat and mat are rhyming words.
The only letter that was changed
is found at the beginning.

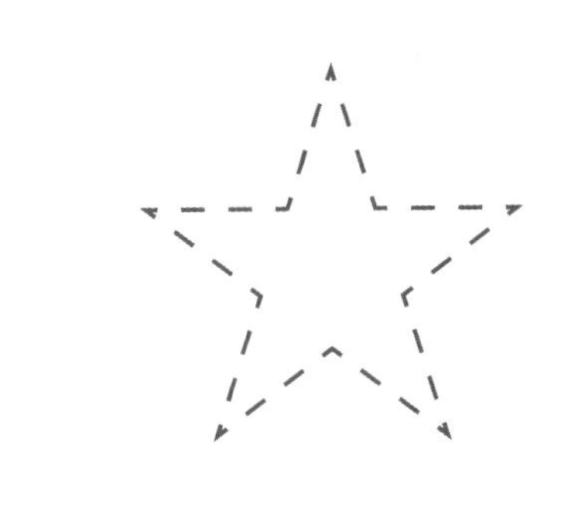

Little Jack Horner

Little Jack Horner sat in a corner,
eating his Christmas pie.
He put in his thumb and pulled out a plum,
and said, "What a good boy am I!"

Trace the lines to make little Jack Horner's pie.

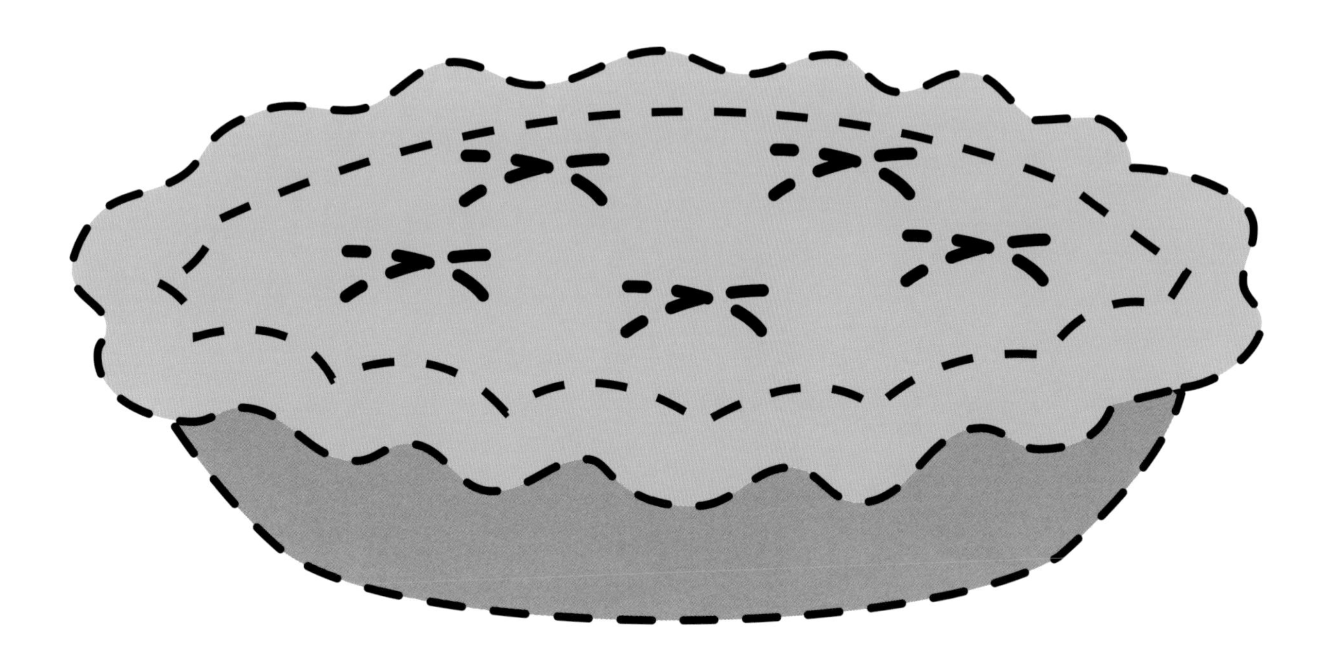

Draw the other half of Little Jack Horner's pie. Color.

Pat-a-Cake, Pat-a-Cake

Pat-a-cake, pat-a-cake baker's man.
Bake me a cake just as fast as you can.
Roll it, pat it, and mark it with a "B".
And put it in the oven for baby and me!

Color the cake.

Circle the items you would use to bake a cake.

Jack and Jill

Jack and Jill went up the hill to fetch a pail of water.
Jack fell down and broke his crown and Jill came tumbling after.

Find Jack and Jill's pail.

Color the ○ **red**. Color the □ **blue**. Color the △ **yellow**.

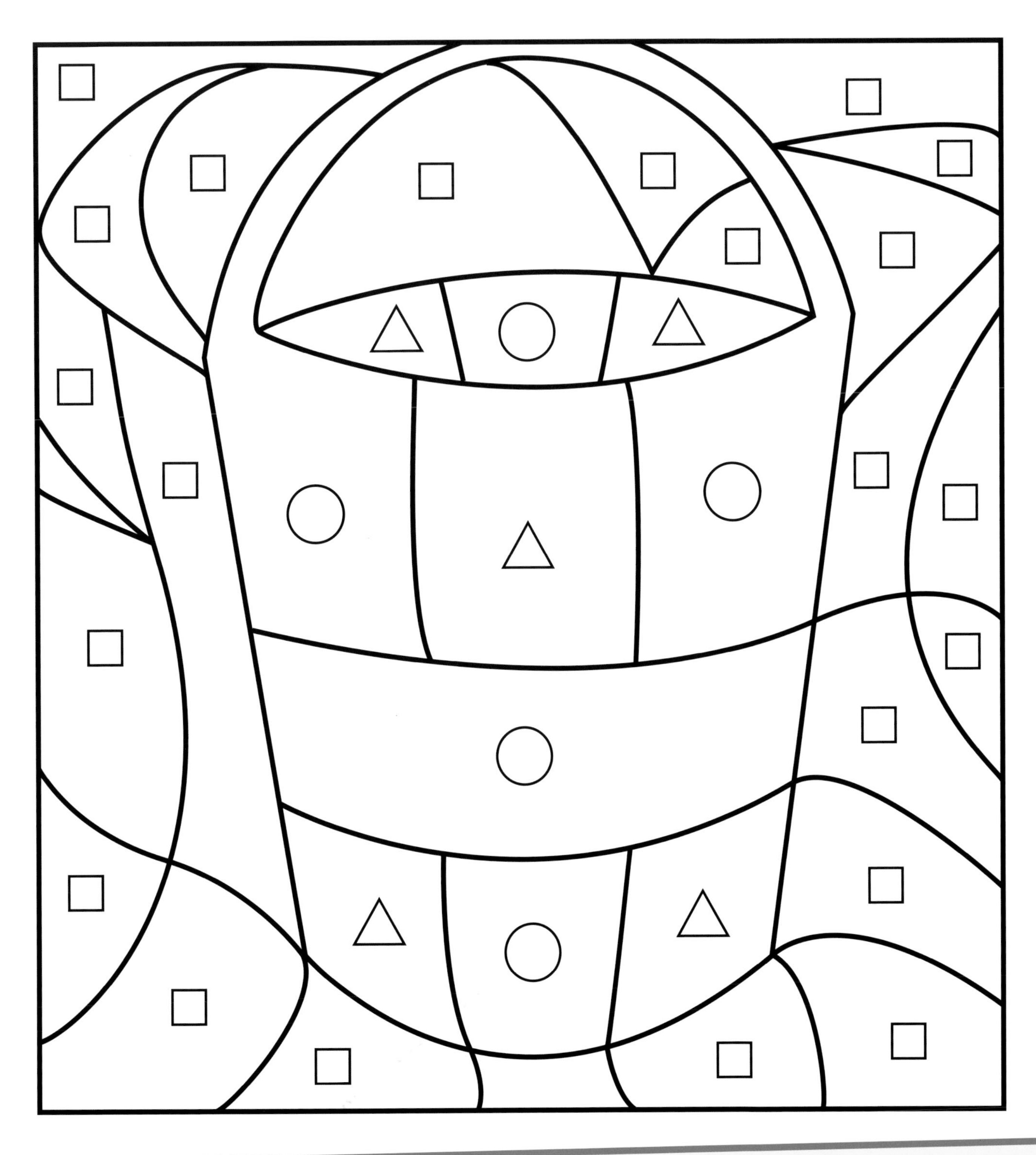

Oh Where, Oh Where Has My Little Dog Gone?

Oh where, oh where has my little dog gone?
Oh where, oh where can he be?
With his ears cut short and his tail cut long,
oh where, oh where can he be?

Help the girl find her lost puppy.

London Bridge

London Bridge is falling down, falling down, falling down.
London Bridge is falling down, my fair lady!